A Chi
Carol

Level 4

Adapted by David A. Hill

Series Editor: Melanie Williams

Pearson Education Limited

Pearson
KAO Two
KAO Park
Harlow
Essex
CM17 9NA

and Associated Companies throughout the world.

ISBN 9781292240145

This adaptation first published by
Penguin Books 2002
7 9 10 8 6
Text copyright © Pearson Education Limited 2002
Illustrations copyright © 2002 Richard Hook/Linden Artists

A Christmas Carol © 1834 Charles Dickens
Adapted by David A. Hill
Series Editor: Melanie Williams
Illustration by Richard Hook
Design by Shireen Nathoo Design

Printed in Great Britain
SWTC/01

Published by Pearson Education Limited

For a complete list of titles available in the Pearson Story Readers series please
write to your local Pearson Education office or contact:
Pearson, KAO Two, KAO Park, Harlow, Essex, CM17 9NA

Answers for the Activities in this book are published in the free Pearson English
Story Readers Factsheet on the website, www.pearsonenglishreaders.com

Contents

CHAPTER 1
Christmas Eve

It was Christmas Eve. London was very cold and foggy. Ebenezer Scrooge was working in his office. His secretary, Bob Cratchit, was writing letters in the next room. It was a very small room, with a very small fire. Bob was very cold. Scrooge did not give Bob much wood for his fire because he did not like to spend money.

Scrooge did not like anything. He did not like the people in the streets or the people he worked with. He did not like eating good food or drinking nice drinks.

He especially hated Christmas.

Scrooge was an old man. He was very thin, with thin, white hair on his head and face. His lips were blue and his eyes were red. He had worked in the same dark office for very many years. Once it had been the office of *SCROOGE AND MARLEY*, and those names were still on the door. But Jacob Marley had died seven years before and Scrooge worked on without him. Work was important. Work brought money, and Scrooge always wanted more money. So Scrooge worked hard, and made Bob Cratchit work hard, too.

Work, work, work!

'A Merry Christmas, uncle,' said Scrooge's nephew, Fred, coming into the cold, dark office.

'Bah!' replied Scrooge. 'Humbug!' He really hated Christmas.

'Oh, come on, uncle,' said Fred. 'I'm sure you don't mean it.'

'I do,' answered Scrooge. 'Why are you merry? You're a poor man.'

'And why aren't you merry?' asked Fred. 'You're a very rich man. And it's Christmas!'

'Bah!' said Scrooge again. 'Humbug!'

'Please come to dinner with us tomorrow, uncle,' said Fred.

'Goodbye,' answered Scrooge.

'I don't want to be angry with you, uncle,' said Fred, 'so Merry Christmas.'

'Goodbye,' said Scrooge again.

Later two men came into Scrooge's office.

'Mr Scrooge? Mr Marley?' asked the first man, who had seen the names on the door.

'Mr Marley died seven years ago,' answered Scrooge.

'Mr Scrooge, then,' said the man. 'At Christmas, it's nice for everyone to give something to people who have nothing – no homes, no clothes, no food.'

'But there are hospitals and other places to help them,' said Scrooge.

'There are,' replied the second man. 'But they always need a little more.'

'It's not my problem,' said Scrooge. 'I've my work to worry about.'

The two men left.

Later a boy came to sing Christmas songs, but Scrooge sent him away.

When it was time to close the office, Bob Cratchit was excited about the holiday next day.

'I imagine you don't want to come to work tomorrow?' said Scrooge to Bob.

'No, sir, I don't,' he answered nervously.

'And you want me to give you money for the whole week?' asked Scrooge.

'Well, Christmas is only one day a year, sir,' replied Bob.

'You're still taking my money for nothing!' said Scrooge. 'Well, if you must, you must. But come to work earlier the morning after.'

That night when Scrooge was at home, he had
a surprise visit. He heard the sound of chains
coming upstairs, and then Jacob Marley walked
through his door.

'Marley!' said Scrooge. 'You're dead! What
do you want from me?'

'I'm a ghost,' said Marley. 'I've been
travelling since I died.'

'Why?' asked Scrooge.

'Because I'm unhappy,' said Marley's ghost.
'I was very bad to people when I was alive, and
I want to help you not to be unhappy like me
when you die.'

'How?' asked Scrooge.

'You'll be visited by three more ghosts,'
answered Marley's ghost.

CHAPTER 2
The First Ghost

The first ghost appeared at one o'clock in the morning, and opened the curtains round Scrooge's bed. The ghost was an old man with long, white hair. He wore a short, brilliant white dress with a bright belt and (a strange thing at Christmas!) summer flowers along the bottom. His arms and legs were bare, and in his hand he held a bunch of green holly.

'I'm The Ghost of Christmas Past,' he said.

'Whose past?' asked Scrooge.

'Your past,' answered the ghost.

'What do you want?' asked Scrooge.

'To help you,' answered the ghost. 'Come'.

Scrooge got up from his bed. Together they flew through the wall and London disappeared. Scrooge saw they were looking at the place in the country where he had lived as a boy.

They saw many boys going home across the fields, happily shouting 'Merry Christmas' to each other. Then they saw Scrooge as a boy, reading on his own in an empty classroom.

Seeing himself as he had once been, Scrooge sat down at a desk and started to cry.

'I wish I'd given some money to that poor boy who sang Christmas songs to me yesterday,' said Scrooge.

The ghost smiled. 'Let's see another Christmas,' he said.

This time Scrooge saw the office where he had first worked. He saw Mr Fezziwig, the man he had worked for, and his wife. Young Scrooge was helping them prepare the office for a Christmas party. Soon there were many young people there. They were enjoying the dancing, the music and the food. Even he, Scrooge, was dancing and enjoying himself!

At the end of the party, Mr and Mrs Fezziwig said 'Merry Christmas' to everybody.

'I wish I'd said something to Bob Cratchit yesterday,' said Scrooge.

The ghost smiled again. 'Another Christmas,' he said.

Scrooge saw a beautiful woman smiling with her children in a warm home.

The door opened and the father came in, his arms full of Christmas presents. Scrooge looked at the woman; she had been his girlfriend when he was a young man! She had left him because he had been more interested in money than in her. Looking at the happy family, Scrooge understood what he had lost.

'No more!' shouted Scrooge sadly. 'Leave me, ghost!'

The first ghost disappeared, leaving Scrooge back in bed where he slept deeply.

Chapter 3
The Second Ghost

Later, Scrooge woke up suddenly. He looked around his bedroom – there was nobody there. He went to the door of his living room.

'Come in, Ebenezer Scrooge,' said a voice.

He opened the door, and saw something very strange. The room looked so different! The walls of the room were covered with Christmas trees and there was a big fire burning. The floor and table were hidden by the most delicious kinds of Christmas foods you can imagine. There was holly all around the room and the green leaves were bright with the light from the fire.

Sitting on top of all the food was a happy young giant, holding a burning torch which lit the room. He was wearing a long, green dress with white fur at the bottom. He had curly brown hair and a hat made of holly.

'Come in, come in,' said the giant. 'I'm The Ghost of Christmas Present.'

'If you've something to teach me,' said Scrooge, 'take me anywhere you want. I learnt a lot from the first ghost.'

'Touch my dress,' said the ghost.

Scrooge did, and soon the trees, the food and the room had disappeared.

Scrooge found they were walking in a London street on Christmas morning. The shops were full of lovely things to eat. Everyone there was happy.

The ghost took him to the Cratchit's house, where they were preparing their small Christmas dinner. Scrooge watched as the poor family ate one goose and some potatoes, and a very small Christmas pudding. They were still as happy as if they had eaten a king's dinner.

Scrooge looked at Tiny Tim, the youngest child, who was ill and could not walk.

'Will he be here next Christmas?' he asked.

'With help,' replied the ghost.

They left the Cratchit's poor but happy house,
and walked through the snowy streets of
London. Everyone was going out to evening
parties with their friends and families. Suddenly
they were in a cold, grey, empty place. Scrooge
and the ghost looked through the window of a
small house. Inside there was a big family in a
small room. They were all singing Christmas
songs together. They were very happy.

'Who are they?' asked Scrooge.

'They are poor miners,' said the ghost. 'People
who work hard inside the Earth we live on.'

17

The ghost took Scrooge back to London, to Scrooge's nephew, Fred's house where there was a big party. Fred was telling everyone about his visit to his uncle.

'When I said "Merry Christmas" to him, he replied "Humbug!"' said Fred.

Everyone laughed.

'He's rich,' said Fred, 'but he doesn't do anything good with his money and he doesn't enjoy Christmas Day. Every year, I'll ask him to our party and wish him "Merry Christmas". Perhaps one day he'll understand, and give some money to poor Bob Cratchit too.'

Scrooge and the ghost watched Fred and his friends all evening.

CHAPTER 4

The Third Ghost

Finally, the ghost took Scrooge home and, as he disappeared, the church clock rang midnight. At once a new ghost appeared, much more frightening than the other two. It was covered from head to toe in a long, black coat.

'You're The Ghost of Christmas Yet to Come,' said Scrooge nervously.

The dark ghost said nothing and did not move.

'I imagine you're going to show me the things which haven't happened yet,' Scrooge said, looking at the strange ghost.

The ghost silently moved its head a little, and pointed with its hand.

Scrooge suddenly found himself in the middle of
the City of London. He saw many of the people
he worked with every day, changing, buying
and selling money.

The ghost stopped and pointed to some men
standing together talking.

'I don't know what happened. I only know
he's dead,' said the first man.

'What's he done with his money?' asked the
second man.

'He didn't give it to me!' said the first man,
laughing.

'His funeral will be very cheap,' said another
man.

'Why?' asked the second man.

'He had no friends. Nobody will go,' answered
the first man.

Scrooge did not understand why the ghost
wanted him to listen to this conversation, but
he knew the ghost did not answer questions, so
he did not ask.

He looked around trying to see himself, but
on the corner where he usually stood at this
time there was another man doing business.

Next the ghost took him to a bad part of
London which he had never been to before.

The streets were small and dark and full of
the poorest people. They went into a dirty shop
full of every horrible old thing you can imagine
– metal, bones, books, clothes . . .

Scrooge watched as three people brought things to sell to the shopkeeper. They were from the same dead man's house.

The first had some small things: buttons and a pencil-case.

'He doesn't need these now,' said the first woman pointing to the towels, silver teaspoons and boots she had.

'Look, Joe,' said the other woman, showing the bed curtains and blankets she had taken from the dead man's bed.

'Is this shirt from the dead body?' asked Joe.

'Yes,' she answered. 'He doesn't need a new shirt now he's dead.'

This could happen to me when I die, thought Scrooge.

Suddenly, Scrooge found himself in another
terrible room. It was very dark, with just a little
light coming through the window.

There was a bed with no curtains on it, and
on the bed, a dead body covered by a sheet.

The ghost pointed to the body, as silent as ever.

Scrooge looked. Who was this dead man?
Why were there no friends or family there to
cry over the body, to feel sad that he had died?
The ghost still pointed. Scrooge understood
it wanted him to look at the face of the dead
man, but he could not.

'I cannot look at this man's face,' said Scrooge. 'But if there's anybody in London who feels something because this man is dead, show them to me.'

The ghost took Scrooge into another room. A woman stood up nervously when her husband came in.

'Is there any news?' she asked.

'When I went to ask him if we could pay the money one week later,' he said, 'an old woman told me he was dead.'

'That's good news,' she said. 'I'm sorry. I mean that now we have time to get the money we have to pay.'

'No, ghost!' said Scrooge. 'I want to see someone who's sorry about a death, not someone who's happy because of one!'

The ghost took him to Bob Cratchit's house. He saw the Cratchit family sitting quietly around the fire. They were talking about Tiny Tim.

'I met Mr Scrooge's nephew, Fred,' said Bob, 'and he said he was very sorry to hear about Tiny Tim.'

Bob turned to his family: 'Let's never forget what a good, gentle boy he was, even if he was just a little child.'

'No, never father!' shouted all the children.

'Tell me, ghost,' said Scrooge. 'Who was the dead man we saw?'

The ghost took him to a churchyard. It was a dark place with the walls of houses all around and no flowers on the graves.

The ghost pointed to one grave.

'Before I look,' said Scrooge, 'tell me if the things we've seen are things which will definitely happen, or only things which may happen?'

The ghost stood in silence.

Scrooge looked at the name on the grave. It said EBENEZER SCROOGE.

'Was I the dead man?' he asked.

The ghost pointed to the grave, then at Scrooge.

CHAPTER 5
Christmas Day

Scrooge fell down, and held the ghost's hand . . .
and woke up to find himself holding the bedpost
of his own bed.

He got dressed quickly, saying to himself:
'Now I'll use the lessons I've learnt from these
three ghosts!'

He laughed. The first time he had laughed for
years!

He saw a boy in the street.

'What day is it today?' he asked.

'It's Christmas Day,' said the surprised boy.

'Go and buy that big turkey from the
butcher's,' said Scrooge. 'There's ten pence for
you!'

I will send it to Bob Cratchit, he thought.

Scrooge walked excitedly along the street saying 'Merry Christmas' to everybody.

When he met the man who had wanted help for the poor the day before, he told him to come and see him to get a lot of money.

Then Scrooge went off to his nephew Fred's house.

Fred was very surprised to see him.

'What do you want, uncle?' he asked.

'I want to come to dinner!' said Scrooge. 'Can I?'

'Of course you can!' answered Fred.

Fred was very happy, and so were his wife and all their friends. And they all had a lovely party together.

CHAPTER 6
Boxing Day

Scrooge went to work very early next morning. He wanted to be in the office before Bob Cratchit got there.

Bob was eighteen minutes late. He was frightened that Scrooge would be angry. He started writing very quickly.

'What's this?' said Scrooge in his old voice. 'Why were you late?'

'I'm very sorry, sir,' said Bob.

'I don't like it!' he shouted. 'So I'm going to . . . '

Bob waited, very frightened.

'. . . I'm going to pay you more money!' said Scrooge, laughing. 'Merry Christmas, Bob.'

Scrooge asked him to go and buy some more wood for the fire.

Chapter 7
Happily Ever After

That afternoon, Scrooge took Bob Cratchit out for a drink and explained how he was going to help him and his family in the future.

Scrooge did everything he said he was going to do and more. He became a friend of the Cratchit family, and he was like a second father to Tiny Tim, who did not die.

Some people laughed at him because he had changed, but Scrooge let them laugh, he did not mind. He knew that there are always people who laugh when good things start happening in the world.

ACTIVITIES

1. In *A Christmas Carol* you will read about three ghosts.
   1 = The Ghost of Christmas Past
   2 = The Ghost of Christmas Present
   3 = The Ghost of Christmas Yet to Come

   Look through the book now, and match the names with the right ghost.

2. Look at the pictures of Ebenezer Scrooge on pages 5 and 29 of the book.
   a. What is different about him?
   b. Why do you think he has changed?

3. Put the sentences below in the same order as they are in the story.
   .... a. Scrooge sees himself when he was a boy at school.
   .... b. Fred asks Scrooge to come to his house for Christmas dinner.

.... c. The ghost of Jacob Marley visits Scrooge.

.... d. Scrooge takes Bob Cratchit for a drink.

.... e. Scrooge sees Bob Cratchit's family having Christmas dinner.

.... f. Scrooge and Bob Cratchit are working in the office on Christmas Eve.

.... g. Scrooge sees his grave in a churchyard.

4. WORDSEARCH

Find the names of five of the characters from *A Christmas Carol* and its author.

E	B	E	N	E	Z	E	R	S	C	R	O	O	G	E
B	O	D	F	H	J	L	C	E	G	I	K	M	O	Q
R	B	J	T	V	X	Z	N	M	P	S	V	W	Y	A
Z	C	A	C	E	G	I	K	R	M	O	R	S	U	W
Y	R	C	Z	H	J	L	N	F	R	E	D	P	R	T
V	A	O	X	B	D	F	H	J	L	E	N	P	Y	Z
C	T	B	E	G	I	K	M	Z	O	R	S	T	R	U
V	C	M	W	Z	Y	X	C	Z	B	A	Y	I	X	W
C	H	A	R	L	E	S	D	I	C	K	E	N	S	A
B	I	R	F	J	M	Q	U	W	A	F	K	Y	O	S
X	T	L	C	H	M	R	W	I	B	H	N	T	T	Z
P	W	E	B	R	I	C	T	G	U	E	N	I	H	O
A	Q	Y	D	J	L	S	F	K	M	P	R	M	V	G